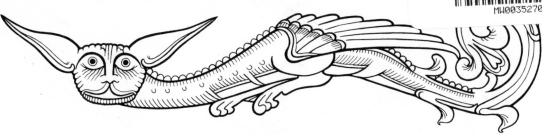

Introduction

There are different sorts of dragons, of different shapes and sizes, and they come from different parts of the world. People say that "except a Serpent eat a Serpent he shall never be a Dragon," and that they grow big by feeding on their own relations. Aristotle adds that apples give dragons indigestion, which they cure by eating wild lettuce.

Once they have reached their full size their diet is more varied, as the stories in this book show. The biggest dragons, which live in India and Ethiopia, ambush elephants by hiding in the trees where they come to browse. Or sometimes two dragons tie their tails together and trip the elephant up as he comes along a path.

Readers of Bellerophon Books need not be afraid of dragons, because we shall tell them simple remedies for dragon-bite, which we found in a *Historie of Foure-Footed Beastes* by Edward Topsell, who lived four hundred years ago in the reign of the first Queen Elizabeth. "The seede of grasse, commonly called Hay-dust, is prescribed against the byting of dragons. The Barble being rubbed upon the place where a Scorpion of the Earth, a Spyder, a Sea or Land-dragon byteth, doth perfectly cure the same. Also the heade of a dogge or dragon which hath bytten any one, beeing cutte off and fleyed, and applied to the wound with a little *Euphorbium*, is said to cure the wound speedily."

Topsell says that "there are dragons of sundry colours, for some of them are blacke, some redde, some of them Ashe-colour, some yellow." We have also found green and blue and golden dragons, so whatever colours you use for the dragons in this book will certainly be right. We hope that you will agree that "their shape and outward appearance is verie beautifull."

Top: from a 12th-cent. Bible, Brit. Lib. MS Roy. I C VII; below: from the *Historie of Foure-Footed Beastes*

2

An Assyrian relief from Nimrud, 9th century B.C. British Museum

Tiamat

The wise men of Babylon used to tell that, before the world and the gods came to be, there was nothing but a waste of waters ruled over by Apsu and Tiamat, from whom perhaps some of the other watery and wicked dragons who appear in this book are descended. Presently the first gods were born, and began to bring order out of the confusion of the universe. Apsu and Tiamat hated them, but the young god of the waters, Ea, was able to slay Apsu (from whose name perhaps comes our word "abyss"). Her body became a great gulf of sweet waters. But Tiamat of the salt waters was unconquered, and with her brood of monsters attacked the gods, who were unable to prevail against her.

At last Ea had a son, Marduk, who was born "in the midst of the holy Apsu," the very place that had been created when Apsu was slain. Marduk from his very birth was "wise in wisdom" and of great strength. The gods met at a banquet, and after feasting and making merry they decided to make Marduk their champion in a war against Tiamat. Marduk consented to lead them if each would confer upon him his own magic powers, and if they would all agree to obey him after the victory was won. When they consented, he asked all to be given some proof of his new powers. So they placed a cloak before him and told him that if he so commanded the cloak would cease to be, and if he gave the word again the cloak would be brought back. And so it was.

Now Marduk made ready to attack Tiamat with lightning and the tempest and the four winds of heaven. Her magic spells had no power over him; he caught her in his net. She opened her mouth to breathe out flames against him, but quickly he let loose the winds and they rushed through her jaws and filled her whole body. As she lay swollen and helpless, Marduk slew her. Then he divided her body in two like a shell fish. From the upper part he made the sky, and from the lower the earth. Now the gods were given their different places in the upper and the lower worlds, and mankind was created from the blood of Tiamat's son in order to serve them. Marduk himself ruled from the great temple that stood in the middle of Babylon.

(From *Enuma Elish*, the Babylonian story of creation)

From a Babylonian seal, Pierpont Morgan Library

4

FARIDUN from the *Shah-nama*, 16th century; Metropolitan Museum of Art

Faridun

Good King Faridun of Persia had three sons who were tall as cypresses and as strong as elephants. But he gave them no names, because he had not made trial of their different qualities. When the time came for them to be married, he sent his envoys through the world to find a king who had three daughters who should be worthy of his sons. The princesses were to be of more than mortal beauty, and so alike that none could tell the difference. And they too must never have been named, so that there could be no tittle-tattle about them.

Only in the kingdom of Araby the Blessed were such princesses to be found, and the wise king their father would not let them go with King Faridun's ambassadors. The three princes had to come themselves to claim their brides.

Joyfully they started their journey home. But when Faridun was told that they were coming he resolved to make trial of them. Taking the form of a dragon so savage that not even a lion might escape it, he advanced on them, breathing flames through the dust-clouds that he stirred up and filling the world with his roaring.

The eldest son, when he charged first, said, "A wise man does not fight dragons," and with that he turned his horse and fled.

The second son took to his weapons and said, "A fight's a fight, no matter whether the enemy is a raging monster or an armed horseman."

FARIDUN'S SONS: Salm, top, the eldest, was given the Kingdom of the West; Tur, bottom, the second son, was given Central Asia and the East......

The third son faced the dragon with a great shout. "Get out of my way, you tom cat! How dare you block the lion's path! If you have heard the name of King Faridun, beware of fighting his sons! Clear the road, and get back to the desert where you belong, or I will crown you in a way that you will not enjoy."

Faridun was pleased, and hurrying home resumed his proper shape, and came to meet his sons again, mounted on his state elephant and with a splendid procession accompanying him. And now he gave each of the princes the name that fitted him, and assigned to each his proper kingdom.

The eldest had shown discretion in choosing safety, and was named Salm, the safe man. To him his father gave the civilized lands of the west.

The second son had shown courage. His father named him Tur, and sent him to rule the Turanians, the fierce wandering horsemen of the east.

But to the third son, who had shown both wisdom and valour, he gave the name Iraj, and his portion was the land of Persia and the plain of heroes, where he ruled over the Iranians.   (From Firdausi, the *Shah Nama.*)

. . . and Iraj, the youngest son, was given Iran.

Saint Michael

The Archangel MICHAEL AND THE DRAGON, 14th-century German; *Kupferstichkabinett*, Berlin-Dahlem

In the Book of Revelation, Michael and his angels fought against the dragon, "that old serpent, called the Devil and Satan," and drove him out from Heaven. For this reason, the Dragon is often regarded as a symbol of wickedness.

SAINT MICHAEL & ANGELS vs. THE DRAGON, from a 13th-century French Apocalypse; *Bibliothèque Nationale fr. 403*; Paris

Saint Margaret

Saint Margaret was the daughter of the Chief Priest of the Pagans in Antioch at the time when the Christians were being persecuted by the Roman Emperors. Her nurse was a Christian, and brought her up in the faith. So her father hated her and she was sent out to live as a shepherdess. One day the Roman Governor Olybrius saw her, and fell in love with her beauty and would have married her. But when he learned that she was a Christian he tortured her and flung her into prison.

And while she was in prison she prayed to Our Lord to make visible to her the fiend that had fought with her. Then there appeared a horrible dragon, and assailed her, and would have devoured her, but she made the sign of the Cross and at once he vanished away. The story is also told that the dragon swallowed her as she made the sign of the Cross, and its body burst and she came out safe and sound. But this swallowing and bursting of the body of the dragon is apocryphal.

(From Caxton's translation of the *Golden Legend* of Jacobus de Voragine.)

SAINT MARGARET after an engraving from a supposedly lost drawing by Martin Schongauer, c. 1480

THE DRAGON OF THE HESPERIDES from an Apulian volute crater, c. 330 B.C. , Ruvo, *Museo Jatta*

Draco

Draco, the Dragon Constellation which shines gloriously in the southern sky on summer nights, is sometimes said to be the dragon which guarded the apple-tree of the Hesperides, the daughters of the Evening Star. Classical geographers tell us that the world of men is surrounded by the ever-flowing stream of Ocean, and beyond that in the furthest West lies the lovely island where it is always spring. Here the Hesperides sit singing in their garden, in the midst of which grows the golden apple-tree, with the great guardian serpent twining through its branches.

Hercules, son of Jupiter and the mortal princess Alcmena, was bound to serve his unworthy cousin King Eurystheus for twelve years. Each year he was set a task—to clear the land of some ravening monster, or to bring back to Eurystheus some famous prize from the ends of the earth. Finally the King ordered him to go even beyond the human world and fetch him the apples of the Hesperides.

All the story-tellers are agreed that he accomplished his task somehow, but there are different accounts of how he did it. In the best-known version he himself got no further than the Ocean's edge, where he set up the Pillars of Hercules that still mark the African and European shores of the Straits of Gibraltar. Here, on the African shore, he found the giant Atlas, who carries the heavens on his shoulders. Atlas said that he would be glad to fetch the apples from the Hesperides, to whom he was closely related, if only someone could be found to support the sky while he was gone. So Hercules undertook this task, and won the apples in this way.

But it was also said that Hercules himself went to the magic island, carried over the Ocean in the golden bowl that bears back the Sun and his team of horses when they have finished their daily journey through the heavens. Some pictures show Hercules laying about him with his club and seizing the apples by force. This story seems to have been made up to explain how the dragon found its way into the heavens: the gods put it there after Hercules killed it. But I would rather believe the pictures that show the hero welcomed as an honored guest, and the dragon, knowing that the stranger has a right to the guarded fruit, quietly coiled about the tree or drinking from a golden saucer which one of its mistresses holds out to it.

(From the *Library* of Apollodorus)

DRACO (or rather Ouroboros) after Michael Maier, *Atlanta Fugiens*, Emblema XIV

Chinese Dragons

Chinese dragons, for all their formidable appearance, are much less dangerous than their relatives in other parts of the world. They live in the water or among the clouds, and, since they can bring the rain or hold it back, they are useful, and indeed necessary. The Dragon is the enemy of the Tiger who is the representative of forests and mountains.

When rain is needed, it is sometimes possible to persuade the dragons to act by throwing tiger bones, or even merely dirt and leaves, into the pools where they dwell. But a polite letter written to the dragon by a Mandarin is probably just as effective.

Liu Ngan says, "Earthen dragons cause the rain to come." This is explained by the story that the Emperor T'ang, who ruled in 1766 B.C., in a time when no rain fell, made a pottery figure of a dragon so that the clouds would follow it. Wang Ch'ung says that the Duke of Cheh in the land of Chu liked dragons and had them painted on all his walls and trays, certainly considering these pictures to be like real dragons. Thus there was always plenty of rain in the country of the Duke.

One must be careful about this sort of thing. Tsu-kao also said that he liked dragons, and had them painted all over his house. "Ah!" he used to say, "What sight can be more pleasant than a dragon?" But one morning a huge scaly green head looked in at his upstairs bedroom window. Tsu-kao bolted downstairs and tripped over the tail of the dragon, which had come in through the hall door. Of course the dragon was only paying a friendly visit, after taking Tzu-kao at his word, and it did him no harm. But everybody agreed that the following summer was unusually wet.

From the Nine Dragon scroll, 13th century; Museum of Fine Arts, Boston

When good Emperors ruled, the natural forces were in harmony with the Empire and the rain fell at the right times and places. But in troubled times the dragons were likely to neglect their duty or make mistakes. During the disturbances before the rule of the T'ang dynasty, Yu Chueh-kung, a great soldier, was riding by himself through a forest. Night came on, and he was glad to see a glimmer of light among the trees. It proved to come from a cottage, where an old woman greeted him and offered him shelter. In the small stable where he put his horse, there was already another splendid animal, far better than Yu would have expected in such a poor place. But he saw no sign of its master, and as the night wore on the old woman became more and more worried.

Yu was troubled by his hostesses's anxiety, and at length she told him that he could set out on a journey through the skies and bring rain to such-and-such a district. Now no rain would fall, and the dragon whose fault it was could be punished. If only the stranger could ride the dragon-horse!

From a jade *pi* disk from
the Chou dynasty; William Rockhill Nelson Gallery of Art

No cavalry general likes to be told that a horse is too much for him, and Yu said that he would ride any horse that was ever foaled, even on a winter night's gallop above the clouds. The old woman gave him a magic comb and told him to use it on the horse's mane when they came above the place where the rain was due. So he mounted, and at once the horse soared up into the darkness. Yu's heart was bold and his seat firm, and soon he recognized the place to which the old woman had told him to go. At once he began to comb out his mount's mane, but he did not realize that a very few touches were all that was needed, and his vigorous combing brought down a great flood.

Chinese emperors often had dealings with dragons. Yu the Great, founder of the Hia dynasty, who lived, as far as I can learn, about the time of the building of the Egyptian Pyramids, was born in the shape of a dragon. He had a carriage drawn by two dragons which had descended in the palace court-yard because of his virtue. He it was who raised the mountains and drew off the waters from the face of the earth, and in this work he was helped by a winged dragon which marked out the canals with its tail.

But even he was troubled by two yellow dragons which threatened to upset his ship while he was crossing the Yangtse River. Everybody was frightened except the Emperor, who laughed and said: "I am appointed by Heaven. I do my best to nourish men. To be born is natural: to die is Heaven's decree. Why be troubled by dragons?" Hereupon the dragons were ashamed and ran away with their tails between their legs.

Three thousand years later, in 756 A.D., Ming Huang of the T'ang dynasty was driven from his capital by the treacherous general An Lu-shan. But a dragon accompanied the poor Emperor and, whenever he had to cross a river, helped him by lifting his boat on its back. The Emperor thanked it and gave it wine.

From a 13th-century Japanese scroll, Kozan-ji, Kyoto

Ming's ancestor, the great Tai Tsung, was troubled by the ghost of a dragon which haunted the Emperor's bedchamber. This dragon had brought rain where it was not wanted, and so the King of the Dragons cut its head off. Tai Tsung had tried to save its life, but perhaps he did not try hard enough.

Among Tai Tsung's generals was that Yu Chueh-kung who had the adventure with the dragon's mother. He offered to guard the door of the bedchamber, and another general, Chin Shu-pao, kept watch with him. Night after night they kept off the ghost, until the Emperor, fearing for their health and safety, set portraits of them at his chamber door, so that the generals might retire to bed and leave the painted sentries to keep watch. This served well enough, until the ghost managed to get in by the back door. Now Wei Cheng the Prime Minister offered himself as a guard, and at last the Emperor was able to sleep secure. Portraits of these three heroes were set up to keep ghosts away from that time on.

The King of the Dragons, though he behaved severely in this story, was often kind. Once he invited sixteen good and holy men to come and dine with him in his palace, beneath the ocean waves. And come they did, some in boats made of leaves, some on the backs of tortoises, or of toads, or sea-monsters.

Text from the T'ang Chronicles and other sources

From a scroll of the Dragon-Boat festival at the summer palace of the Han emperors, 14th century; Metropolitan Museum of Art

A China Town celebration, from an 18th-century dish in the Victoria & Albert Museum

California's own Dragon is a friendly and helpful beast. He is carried in procession through the streets of San Francisco as part of the celebration of the Chinese New Year. This procession of the Dragon on the fifteenth day of the first month is a very ancient custom, and is meant to bring rain at the right times to ensure a good harvest in the coming year.

Beowulf

Beowulf in his youth delivered the Spear-Danes from Grendel, a monster who lived beneath the waters of a desolate mere. Later he became king of his own nation, the Geats. For fifty years he ruled well, but then there came against his people a fiery dragon, and the manner of his coming was this:

Long and long ago an old man, the last of his race, had buried his kinsmen's treasures in a stone chamber under a mound on a lonely moor. When the guardian was dead, the ancient foe who comes in the dusk, the slippery dragon who flies by night, wrapped in flame, was fated to seek out the hoard beneath the earth. There, ancient in winters, he guarded the heathen gold, yet was nothing the better for it. Three hundred years he watched, and then while he was sleeping there came to the treasure-house a runaway slave, who carried off a single golden cup to buy his master's forgiveness. When the dragon woke, first he hurried out on the man's tracks, then he turned back to hunt again for the cup. He longed for the day to end, so that he could leave his mound, bringing fire with him. All night he laid waste the land of the Geats, but before daylight he hurried back to his barrow. So Beowulf roused himself to fight a last battle for his people. He knew that no shield of linden-wood could help him, so he had a shield all of iron made against the dragon's flame. With twelve chosen companions he came to the den, guided unwillingly by the wretched man who had stolen the cup. Sitting on the sea-cape facing the barrow, Beowulf told of the great deeds of his youth, then rose and went forward to the stone arch through which a stream broke out of the mound, hot with fire. Here he could go no further, but sent his war-cry ringing through the rocks to rouse the dragon.

First there came out of the rock the beast's vapor, the hot breath of battle. The earth rang, and the hero below the mound raised his shield. Then came the dragon itself, coil upon coil. Beowulf swung the sharp sword that he had inherited from his ancestors, but the blade would not bite on the dragon's bone. And now the monster breathed out flames all about the hero, and his companions, thinking that he was lost, took to their heels and hid in the woods—all but one of the twelve. Wiglaf, the king's kinsman, ran to the rescue, just as Beowulf's sword broke on the dragon's head and the monster seized the king by the throat. But now Wiglaf struck it lower down, plunging

From fittings on a horse harness found in boat grave 6, Valsgärde, Uppland, Sweden; 7th century A.D. They were made in the same locale as the shield fitting, opposite, found in the Sutton Hoo boat grave.

his whole blade into the dragon, so that its fires began
to sink, and the king, recovering, drew his glaive, keen
and sharp for battle, that he wore over his armor,
and cut the dragon in two.

But the dragon's poison burned in him from his
wound. As he lay dying, he bade Wiglaf bring out to
him some of the dragon's gold, so that he could
comfort himself with the thought of the treasure.
Then he died, and when the cowards came skulking
back one by one Wiglaf sent them to summon the
people, and buried Beowulf high upon the sea-cliffs
with the dragon-gold about him, as useless to men as
it had been before.

(From *Beowulf*, a story that was probably
brought to England soon after the Saxons began to
settle in the country, though the poem in which it is
told is rather later, and seems to have been made up
about 700 A.D.)

A DRAGON AND GENTLEFOLK from about the time of BEOWULF,
from items found in the ship burial at Sutton Hoo, 7th century A.D.
The Dragon, right, is reduced from a shield fitting; the warriors, above,
restored and enlarged, are from the helmet fragments; British Museum.

Melusine

Once upon a time there was a Count of Anjou who journeyed far and long in foreign parts. But he had no Countess to grieve for him at home, and perhaps his vassals were quite as happy left to their own devices as they would have been with a lord who kept strict watch over their doings. Be that as it may, there was at least a show of general rejoicing when the Count suddenly returned, bringing with him a lady of exceptional beauty who shortly afterwards, to no one's surprise, became his wife.

Melusine of Anjou was not only beautiful; she did everything that a Countess ought to do, winning the hearts of great and small by her charming manners and providing her husband with four children to carry on his line. But nobody knew where she came from—perhaps not even the Count: at all events he had nothing to say about his wife's home and parents, though anybody could see that she was of noble lineage and very rich. And at tournaments no strange knights entered the lists to break a lance in honour of their kinswoman the Countess; at banquets though the troubadours had travelled far and wide, none had songs to sing about the distant country from which the Countess came.

So it went on for some years, and at last people began to whisper that, however perfect the Countess's behaviour in other respects, she set a very poor example as a churchwoman. Not only did she go to church very seldom, but when she did go she always managed to slip away before the priest showed the consecrated chalice to the congregation. Her husband the Count at length determined that there should be no more of this, and told four of his knights to see to it that the next time his lady remained until the end of the service. Sure enough, next Sunday the Countess went to church with her children about her, but at the critical moment, she made some excuse and prepared to slip out as usual. However, this time the knights stood firmly on her hem, so that she could not get away. Hereupon with a dreadful shriek she burst the fastenings, left her dress behind her, turned into a dragon, and flew out of the window, dragging along two of her children. Centuries later, she was still sometimes seen in dragon form flying round Melusine's Tower in the Castle of Lusignan.

Female dragons are unusual, except in India and China. It gives special pleasure to record one who is an ancestress of most of the Crowned Heads of Europe. For from Melusine's surviving children derives the House of Plantagenet, whose descendants eventually married into almost every royal family from St. Petersburg to Lisbon.

(From Giraldus Cambrensis, a distinguished civil servant, historian and churchman under the Plantagenet kings)

From *Voeux du Paon*, Glazier MS. 24, Pierpont Morgan Library, New York; 14th century

GEOFFREY COUNT OF ANJOU from his effigy at Le Mans, 12th century

Perseus

Cassiopeia, Queen of Ethiopia, had a daughter, Andromeda, who was so beautiful that her mother boasted that she was fairer than the sea-nymphs. Naturally the nymphs complained to Neptune, and he flooded the land and sent a sea-dragon to lay it waste. Cepheus, Andromeda's father, sent to the oracle to ask how the angry dogs could be turned aside, and learned that nothing would serve but that he should take his daughter, dressed in all her finery as a bride, and chain her to a rock by the sea-shore for the monster to devour. So amid weeping and wailing the princess was led out of the city. Iron chains were fastened to her tender wrists and ankles; huge spikes were driven into the cliff, and she was fastened to the face of the rock.

But just as her parents were turning away in tears a distant figure was seen flying swiftly through the air. It drew near, and in an instant a handsome young man stood on the sea-shore. This was Perseus, prince of Mycenae, who had been given winged sandals and sword of sharpness by the god, so that he could fly across the ocean and cut off the head of Medusa the Gorgon. He was now on his way home after accomplishing his tasks.

Seeing the maiden chained to the rock, he fell instantly in love and swooped down to her rescue. But before he could do more than declare his love there was a sudden disturbance in the waters, and far away appeared the jagged back of the dragon, with waves foaming white about it as it cut through the sea straight towards Andromeda.

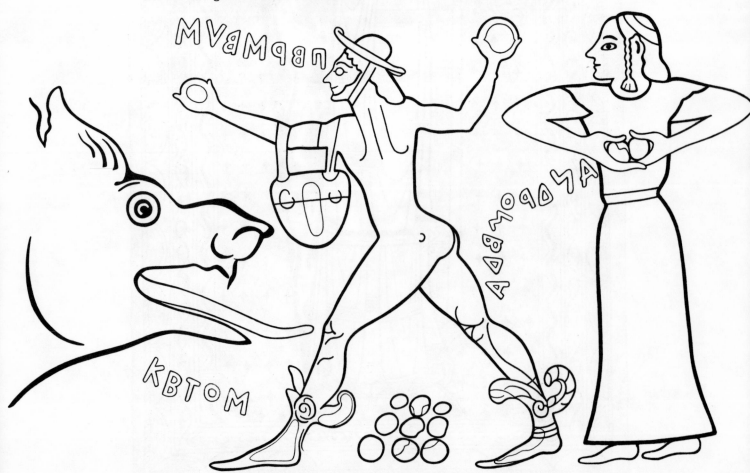

PERSEUS and ANDROMEDA throwing stones at the Dragon, from a Corinthian vase, c. 550 B.C.   Berlin

Perseus sprang into the air, and the winged sandals carried him high above the dragon. Swooping down, he struck again and again with the sword of sharpness, until the sea was red with the monster's blood. Then he cut through the chains, and rescued Andromeda to be his bride.

Some people say that Perseus turned the dragon into stone, through the magic power of the Gorgon's head, and that it lies in the sea as a great reef to this day. But Cassiopeia, Perseus and Andromeda were all eventually taken up into the heavens and changed to stars, and the astronomers say that the dragon is there too, and name him, Cetus, the sea-monster.

(From Ovid's *Metamorphoses*)

PERSEUS AND ANDROMEDA from St. John's College MS 208, Cambridge; 15th century

Saint George

Beside the city of Sylene in Libya was a swamp or lake where lived a dragon that poisoned all the countryside. The people came together to kill it, but when they saw it they ran away. And when the dragon came near the city its breath poisoned them. So every day they brought the dragon two sheep to eat, to keep it from doing any harm. Then there were so few sheep left that they began to send a man and a sheep. At last they made a law that the children of the town should be chosen by lot, and that everyone on whom the lot fell, rich and poor alike, should be delivered to the dragon.

Then the lot fell on the king's daughter, and he was sorrowful, and said to the people, "For God's love, take gold and silver and all that I have, only leave me my daughter." "How is this, Sire?" they said. "You made the law Your daughter shall be given, or we will burn you and your house."

When the king saw that he could do no more, he began to weep, and said to his daughter, "Now shall I never see your wedding." Then he returned to the people and asked to be granted eight days, and this they granted him. And when the eight days were past, they came to him and said, "You see that the city is dying." Then the king dressed his daughter in her wedding dress, and kissed her and gave her his blessing and led her to the place where the dragon was.

When she came to the place, Saint George, a knight of Cappadocia and a Christian, rode by. He saw the princess, and asked her why she was there. She answered, "Go your way, fair sir, so that you may not perish too." Then he said, "Tell me your story, and why you are weeping. Fear nothing." When she saw that he was resolved to know, she told him how she was delivered to the dragon. Then said Saint George, "Fair daughter, trust me in this. For I shall help you in the Lord's name." She said, "For God's sake, good knight, go on your way, for you cannot save me." As they spoke together, the dragon appeared and came running towards them. Saint George sprang on his horse and drew his sword and made the sign of the cross to protect himself. Then he rode boldly against the dragon as it came towards him, and struck the dragon with his spear and wounded it and threw it to the ground. After this he said to the maid, "Give me your girdle, and bind it about the neck of the dragon, and be not afraid." When she had done so, the dragon followed her as if it had been a tame and gentle beast. She led it into the city, and the people fled over hill and dale saying, "Alas! Alas! We shall all be dead!" But Saint George said to them, "Fear nothing! believe in the Lord and be baptised, and I will slay the dragon." Then the king was baptised and all his people, and Saint George slew the dragon and smote off its head, and commanded that the dragon should be thrown into the fields. And the people took four ox-carts and drew the dragon out of the city.

(From Caxton's translation of the *Golden Legend* of Jacobus de Voragine)

SAINT GEORGE and the DRAGON, after the Master of the Barefoot Altar, 15th century; *Landesmuseum*, Hanover

Saint George was a brave Roman soldier who was put to death in 303 A.D. by the Roman Emperor Diocletian when he declared himself a Christian.

William of Malmesbury, an English chronicler, says that Saint George appeared to the Crusaders at the siege of Antioch in 1097 A.D. This may have been the start of his popularity in England. Nowadays, as everybody knows:

"This blessed and holy martyr Saint George is patron of this realm of England, and the battle-cry of its men of war. In his worship has been founded by the Kings of England the noble order of the Garter, and also a noble college in the Castle of Windsor. In this college is the heart of Saint George, which Sigismund the Emperor of Almayne brought and gave for a great and precious relic to King Harry the Fifth."

An old song says:

Harry the Fifth, he conquered all France,

And quartered their arms, his honor to advance;

He their cities razed and threw their castles down,

And his head he honored with a double crown:

He thumped the Frenchmen, and after home he came,

But St. George, St. George he did the dragon tame.

St. George he was for England, St. Denis was for France,

Sing *Honi soit qui mal y pense*.

(From William Caxton's translation of the *Golden Legend* of Jacobus de Voragine and Thomas Percy's *Reliques of Ancient Poetry*.)

ST. GEORGE & THE DRAGON after C. Crivelli, mid-15th century; Metropolitan Museum of Art

SAINT MICHAEL again, dealing with the DRAGON; after the Master of Saint Sebastian, c. 1500; *Musée Calvet*, Avignon

The Dragon of Rhodes

When the Saracens prevailed over the Crusaders and forced them to leave the Holy Land, the Knights of Saint John found a new home on the island of Rhodes. Here below Saint Stephen's Hill, about two miles from the city, was a spring of water, and near it lived a great dragon. Sheep, cattle and horses that came to the pool to drink were devoured, and sometimes an unwary shepherd would fall a victim. Knight after knight vowed to rid the island of the monster, and rode out to do battle with it. But none ever returned, and at last the Grand Master commanded that, should any be so bold as to attack the dragon again, and live to tell of it, he should be expelled from their Order and made a servant.

Now there was a certain knight of Languedoc named Dieudonné de Gozon who had more than once watched the dragon from a safe distance but had never offered to do battle with it. Some of his companions whispered that he lacked courage, and when he asked the Grand Master for leave of absence to visit his home most people thought that he wished to escape the sneers. But he had something else in mind.

Once he was out of sight of the Grand Master, he made a model dragon, the same size as the real one, and as like it as possible. Every day he rode to attack the model, with the aid of two huge mastiffs. Sir Dieudonné had seen, when he watched the dragon, that its under-side was not protected with scales, and so he trained his dogs to attack this part of the model by fastening pieces of meat beneath it. And his horse, which had at first shied away from the gaping jaws and scaly back, became used to them and faced the pasteboard dragon boldly.

When all seemed ready, Sir Dieudonné took ship secretly for Rhodes, with his dogs, his charger and two faithful squires. Bidding the squires watch from a distance, and not attempt to rescue him if he failed in his attempt, he rode down to the dragon's spring with the mastiffs trotting at his horse's heels.

When the real dragon rushed out the horse found it very different from the model and tried to bolt. Sir Dieudonné sprang down and attacked on foot, but was laid low by a blow from the huge tail. He would have been lost, if his dogs had not sprung to the rescue and attacked as they were trained to do. This gave the knight time to rise, and as the dragon reared up to crush him he wounded it mortally with his sword. But he was pinned beneath the huge body as it fell, and would have perished too if the squires had not gone to his help, seeing that the dragon was dead.

Not finding a Dragon of Rhodes, we borrowed a venomous serpent from the Knights' next base at Malta, where they went after retiring from Rhodes at the Turks' behest. This is from a vase made to contain Maltese soil sold to protect people from poisonous beasts, such as Saint Paul had once conquered there.

The people of the countryside gathered and would have brought Sir Dieudonné in triumph into the city. But he presented himself before the Grand Master and acknowledged that he had disobeyed his commands. So he was stripped of his knight's robe, the spurs were hacked from his heels and he was cast out of the Order. But the Master had no wish to disgrace the Dragon-slayer for long. Dieudonné was soon restored to his rank, and when the Grand Master died, was chosen to succeed him, in 1346 A.D.

Three hundred years later the dragon's head was still to be seen above one of the gates of the city.

(From the Abbé de Vertot, *Histoire des Chevaliers Hospitaliers*)

A KNIGHT OF RHODES after Pintoricchio, c. 1500; *Duomo*, Siena

Hercules and the Hydra

The Hydra was the child of Typhon and Echidna, snaky enemies of the gods. It had nine heads, of which eight were mortal but one immortal, and made its home in a great pool of water that gushed up at the foot of a hill at Lerna, a few miles from where Hercules lived. From here it raided the countryside, devouring flocks and herds and people alike. So strong was its venom that its very breath was fatal.

The third Labour that King Eurystheus laid upon Hercules was to rid the land of the Hydra. So Hercules mounted his chariot, driven by his friend Iolaus, and drove down to Lerna. His arrows roused the monster, and as it came out to attack him he set about it with his club, or (so some people say) began cutting its heads off with a great sickle.

But for each head he cut or crushed two more grew, and moreover he was distracted by a monstrous crab that crawled out of the sea and began to nip his ankle. Hercules soon disposed of the crab, but since the Hydra had an ally, he thought that he could fairly call for help himself, and summoned Iolaus, who was watching beside the chariot.

Iolaus saw what was wanted, and set alight a neighboring wood, from which he snatched up firebrands as he hurried to the fight. Now as fast as

IOLAUS AND HERCULES FIGHTING THE LERNAEAN HYDRA
From a Caeretan black-figure hydria, or water jug, from the 6th century B.C. Private collection, London

Hercules cut a head off his friend put a blazing torch to the stump of the neck, and the fire stopped the new heads from growing. Thus all the mortal heads were disposed of in the end. As for the immortal one, Hercules cut off that too, and since he could not kill it he buried it beneath a rock so huge that only he could move it. Then he took his arrows and dipped them in the blood of the Hydra, so that the venom might poison his enemies.

We are not told how Hercules and Iolaus had escaped the poison during the fight, but Hercules was to fall victim to it in the end. For he shot with his arrows the centaur Nessus who had attacked his wife, and Nessus as he lay dying told her to dip a shirt in his blood and give it to her husband if ever she feared that he was false to her. But the centaur's blood carried the poison of the Hydra, and when, years later, Hercules did indeed put on the shirt of Nessus, it burned him like fire, and he was only delivered from his torment when his body was consumed on a funeral pyre and his soul went up to dwell among the gods.

The crab too reached the heavens, some people say. For Juno, who hated Hercules, rewarded the crab for fighting him by setting it among the stars as Cancer, the fourth sign of the Zodiac..

(From the *Library* of Apollodorus)

The Dragon of Wantley

Old stories tell, how Hercules
A dragon slew at Lerna,
With seven heads, and fourteen eyes,
To see and well discern-a:
But he had a club, this dragon to drub,
Or he had ne'er done it, I warrant ye:
But More of More-Hall, with nothing at all,
He slew the dragon of Wantley.

All sorts of cattle this dragon did eat.
Some say he ate up trees,
And that the forests sure he would
Devour up by degrees:
For houses and churches were
　　to him geese and turkies;
He ate all, and left none behind,
　　But some stones, dear Jack,
　　that he could not crack,
Which on the hills you will find.

The poet tells how the dragon
met his match in a "furious knight"
who lived nearby, and "did engage
　　To hew the dragon down;
But first he went, new armor to
Bespeak at Sheffield town;
With spikes all about,
　　not within but without,
Of steel so sharp and strong:

Both behind and before, arms, legs, and all o'er,
Some five or six inches long.
"Had you but seen him in this dress,
How fierce he look'd, and how big,
You would have thought him for to be
Some Egyptian porcupig;
He frightened all, cats, dogs, and all,
Each cow, each horse, and each hog:
For fear they did flee, for they took him to be
Some strange outlandish hedge-hog.

It is not strength that always wins,
For wit doth strength excell;
Which made our cunning champion
Creep down into a well;
Where he did think this dragon would drink;
And so he did in truth;
And as he stoop'd low,
　　he rose up and cry'd boh!
And hit him in the mouth.

Finally the knight jumped out and
gave the dragon a kick at the root
of his tail.
　　Murder, murder, the dragon cry'd,
　　Alack, alack, for grief;
　　Had you but mist that place, you could
　　Have done no mischief.
So the dragon was conquered at last.

The real "Dragon of Wantley" was a Yorkshire squire who three hundred years ago tried to cheat his neighbors of their rights. More of More-Hall, the hero of the story, brought a law-suit against him (the prickly "suit" of armor in which the knight dressed) and beat him. The song was made up in imitation of the old ballads of Saint George and the Dragon.

(From Thomas Percy's *Reliques of Ancient Poetry*)

From the broadside *Ballad of the Dragon of Wantley*, n.d.

The Prince and the Dragon

Once upon a time there was an Emperor who had three sons, who were all fine young men and fond of hunting.

One morning the eldest prince rode out to hunt in a neighboring forest, where wild animals of all sorts were to be found. Suddenly a hare started out of a thicket in front of him. The young man gave chase over hill and dale, until at last the hare came to a riverside and took refuge in a mill that stood by the stream. The prince followed without thinking, but when he came to the door he stopped in terror, for instead of a hare there stood before him a dragon, breathing fire and flame. The prince turned to fly, but a fiery tongue coiled round his waist and drew him into the dragon's mouth and he was seen no more.

A week passed, and when the prince never came back everyone became uneasy. At last the second brother told his father that he too would go hunting, and would perhaps find what had become of his brother. But hardly had the castle gates closed behind him than the hare sprang out of the bushes as before, and once again the chase led over hill and dale until the hare ran into the mill with the prince at his heels. Then instead of the hare there stood a dragon breathing fire and flame, and out shot a fiery tongue which coiled round the prince's waist and lifted him into the dragon's mouth and he was seen no more.

Days went by, and the Emperor waited and waited, and could not sleep at night for wondering about his sons. At last the youngest son begged his father to be allowed to go in search of his brother, and though the Emperor was very unwilling to let him go, at last he gave him permission.

No sooner was he on his way than the hare started up, and led him the same chase that it had led his brother. But when they came to the mill, the young prince was wiser than his brother, and turned away, saying to himself that there were as good hares as this in the forest.

For many hours he rode up and down the mountain, but found nothing, and at last he came back to the mill. Here he found neither hare nor dragon, but an old woman seated outside. The prince greeted her, and asked about his hare. "My son," replied the old woman, "that was no hare, but a dragon, who has led many men hither and then has eaten them all." "Alas!" cried the prince, "Then my brothers must have suffered this fate."

"You have guessed right," answered the old woman, "and my best advice to you is to go home at once before the same happens to you." Then let me take you with me," said the prince; but the old woman said that she too was the dragon's prisoner and could not escape.

"Then when he comes home coax him to tell you the secret of his strength, and tell me when I return," said the prince, and this the old woman agreed to do. So the prince left her.

When the dragon came home, the old woman flattered him and said how much she loved his strength. If only she knew where it lay, she would run and kiss the place! So first the dragon told her his strength lay in the hearthstone, and when she ran to kiss it he laughed at her, and said, "My

strength lies in a lake, and in this lake lives a dragon, and inside the dragon is a wild boar, and inside the wild boar is a pigeon, and inside the pigeon is a sparrow, and inside the sparrow is my strength." And he laughed to think that never, never could his strength be taken from him.

When the dragon left home next morning, the young prince returned to the mill and the old woman told him what she had learned. He listened in silence, and then went home, and, dressing himself as a shepherd, wandered through the world until he came to the kingdom of which the dragon had spoken. Here he presented himself to the king and offered to herd his sheep. The king told him that beside the lake outside his city lay the richest meadows in the kingdom. His flock would run straight to them, but he must beware, for none that had gone that way had ever returned.

With a low bow the prince promised to heed His Majesty's words. Then he went to the market and bought two greyhounds, a hawk, and some shepherd's pipes.

Next morning when he led his flock out the sheep ran straight to the meadow by the lake. The prince did not try to stop them, but walked into the water calling out "Dragon! Dragon! If you are not a coward, come out and fight with me!" A voice answered from the depths, "I am waiting for you, O prince," and the next minute the dragon reared himself out of the water, huge and horrible to behold.

They wrestled until the sun was high, and then the dragon gasped, "Let me but dip my burning head in the lake, and I will hurl you higher than the sky." And the prince replied, "If the king's daughter were but here and would kiss me on the forehead, I would hurl you higher still." Then the dragon loosed his hold and sank back into the lake.

In the evening, the prince collected his sheep and went back into the city, piping in front of them, with his hounds at his heels and his hawk on his shoulder. All the people wondered, for never before had any shepherd returned from the lake.

Next day all happened as before, but this time the prince was watched by two horsemen who had been sent by the king, and told him all that he had seen and heard. The king bade his daughter fear nothing, but to go with the strange shepherd on the third day and do as he asked.

So on the third day the brave princess went with the shepherd, and stood watching while he waded into the lake. "Dragon, dragon, if you are not a coward, come forth, and let us have one more fight," called the prince. And the voice came from the depths, "I am waiting for you, O prince," and next moment the dragon reared out of the water, huge and horrible to behold. Again they wrestled until the sun was high, but this time when the prince wished for the king's daughter to kiss him on the forehead, quickly she ran in and kissed him. Then with a mighty heave he threw the dragon up to the clouds, and when it fell to earth it broke into a thousand pieces.

From the pieces sprang a wild boar, and the prince let slip his greyhounds, which pulled the boar down. The prince cut it open, and there flew out a pigeon. This time the prince let fly his hawk, and in the pigeon he found a

sparrow. "Spare me," said the sparrow as it fluttered in his hand, "and I will tell you how to release your brothers and the other prisoners in the mill."

So the prince was able to rescue his brother and a multitude of men and women who had been trapped by the dragon. Then he married the princess and lived happily ever after.

(Serbian folktale, condensed from Andrew Lang, *The Crimson Fairy-book*.)

Cadmus

Nowadays when someone does something that is likely to have dangerous consequences that he does not expect we say that he is "sowing dragon's teeth". This is the story from which the saying comes.

Zeus, the chief of the gods, changed himself into a bull and carried off the Princess Europa on his back. Her three brothers went in search of her, and one of them, Cadmus, came to Greece. He found no trace of his sister, so he asked the Oracle at Delphi for help. The Oracle told him to follow a cow, which he would meet after he left the shrine, and to found a city where it stopped. The cow went on and on, and at last it rested by a spring. Here lived a mighty dragon, the guardian of the water, and before Cadmus could build his city he had to slay the dragon. Now came the question of where he was to find people for his city, and the goddess Athena advised him to plough the land and sow the teeth of the dragon. All at once there was a stirring in the furrows, and then a gleam of bronze: first spear-points came up, and then tops of helmets; and soon there came up from the ground a great host of savage warriors who began to look about for enemies to kill. Cadmus was afraid he would be the first victim, but Athena again advised him, and he tossed a pebble into the crowd, which struck one of the bronze helmets. The warrior turned fiercely on his neighbor and accused him of striking the blow: others took sides in the quarrel and soon all the dragon-men were fighting each other. When the battle was over only five were left alive, and from these five were descended the five chief families of the new city of Thebes. Hundreds of years later, the men of these families still painted dragons on their shields, to show that they came from the race born from the dragon's teeth.

(From the *Library* of Apollodorus)

MEDEA, who appears in the next story, from British Museum Royal MS. 20, 14th century

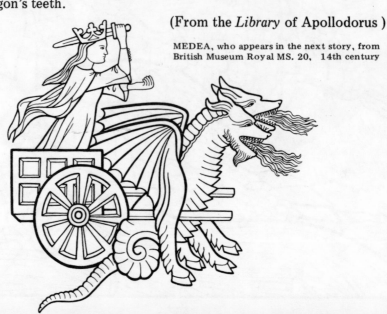

CADMUS AND THE DRAGON OF THEBES, from a Spartan dish, *Musée du Louvre*, Paris

Jason

In the land of Thessaly there lived a boy and a girl, Phrixus and Helle, whose wicked stepmother sought to put them to death. But the gods rescued them, and they were carried away on the back of a golden ram. As they crossed the sea, Helle fell into the strait that is still called after her the Hellespont and was drowned. But Phrixus came safely to the land of Colchis, far away under Mount Caucasus. Here the king of the country, Aeetes, was told by an oracle to sacrifice the ram and hang its fleece upon a tree, and guard it carefully, for if ever it were carried off by a stranger his own death was sure.

Aeetes hung the fleece in a sacred grove, fenced about with a high wall, and guarded by a monstrous dragon which never slept. Medea, the king's daughter, who was an enchantress, was also keeper of the dragon, and used to bring it honey cakes and caress its scaly head.

At last there came to Colchis in quest of the fleece Jason, in his magic ship Argo, on which most of the heroes of Greece had embarked as crew. With their help he had safely passed through many adventures on the voyage, and now he was to find help once more. For—so the goddess Venus contrived it—Medea herself fell in love with him, and by her magic he was able to perform the tasks that the king had set him. But still Aeetes would not give up the fleece, and at last Medea told Jason that she would help him to steal it, if he would carry her away to Greece and make her his bride.

At dead of night they made their way to the grove. All at once Jason saw a light like a blazing star hanging in the air high above his head. This, Medea told him, was the sleepless eye of the dragon. She laughed, and asked if he would rather fight the monster with his weapons or let her charm it with her spells.

Jason stood helpless, and without waiting for his answer Medea began to sprinkle magic herbs and sing her incantations. The great coils lowered themselves from the tree: the scaly back sank down, and little by little the fiery eyes were closed.

Then Medea remembered how in former days she had cared for the dragon and brought it sweetmeats. Now she had deceived it, and miserable would be its awakening when it found its treasure gone. But at least she had not killed it, and she hoped that it might escape to live out its life in some other grove.

Jason still did not dare to approach the tree. But Medea bade him climb boldly, making the dragon's back his ladder. Up he sprang and seized the fleece, and a moment later they were both hurrying down to the ship where the heroes awaited him.

(After Valerius Flaccus, *Argonautica*—a poem written slightly before 100 A.D. The picture, from a cup painted at Athens about 490 B.C., illustrates another version of the story which is now lost. The dragon has swallowed Jason, but by the help of the goddess Athena who stands before him he is being delivered from its jaws. The Golden Fleece hangs on a tree in the background.)

IASON

The Dragon guarding the Golden Fleece disgorges Jason; from a cup painted by Douris, c. 470 B.C. Vatican Museum

Melusine Again

About two hundred years after the first story of Melusine was written down, a different tale was told, which was perhaps more pleasing to the great men whose families were connected with her. In this version she was a fairy. Her father had ill-treated her mother, so by her magic power she shut him up in a great mound of earth where the gray North Sea breaks on the rock-bound Northumbrian coast. But children should not take it upon themselves to punish their fathers, and the Queen of Fairies punished Melusine in her turn. Every Saturday she was turned into a dragon from the waist down, and had to free herself of her tail by secretly taking a magic bath. But she could be rid of her punishment once and for all if she could find a husband who would agree never to see his wife on a Saturday.

Finding a husband was an easy matter for a girl as beautiful as Melusine with all the gowns and jewels of a fairy wardrobe. Soon a handsome young nobleman was at her feet, ready to promise anything if only she would be his. But young men sometimes find that, though they have the best intentions before marriage, it is neither so easy nor so convenient to keep promises when the time comes. So it was in this case. By her magic power Melusine brought her husband lands, wealth and castles. But as time went on he became more and more curious about what his wife did every Saturday, when she retired to her great tower and locked herself in.

Still, as he most sincerely loved her and she loved him in return, their marriage was happy, and the beautiful young Countess and her lovely

MELUSINE from a woodcut by Gerhard Leeu, Antwerp, 1491

Foulk Nerra, COUNT OF ANJOU, 987-1040

children were the talk of the countryside. But alas! not all the talk was good-natured. If the Count did not know what his wife was doing, how did he know that she was not up to some wickedness? Did he really know anything about her at all? Where did she come from? Was she not perhaps a wicked witch who sat up in her tower, overlooking the whole countryside and casting her spells? Who would protect the people from sorcery if their lord the Count failed to do his duty?

So, as too often happens, the Count persuaded himself that it was indeed his duty to do what he wanted to do, and satisfy his curiosity, promise or no promise. One fatal Saturday he crept up the twisting stone stair to his wife's secret chamber and put his eye to a knot-hole in the door. There sat Melusine in her bath, and—horrors!—below the waist she was a monstrous scaly dragon. The Count's cry of fear and disgust told Melusine that she was discovered and all was lost. With a yet more heartrending cry of her own she took the dragon shape that she was doomed to keep for evermore and flew away.

But she comes back, to hover over her tower with sad cries, whenever one of her descendents is going to die in the Castle.

(From Jean d'Arras, *Melusine*)

Rustam

Long ago, in the days of the foolish King Kai Kaus of Persia, Rustam the great hero had to journey to the land of Mazanderan to deliver the King and all his army from the demons who had made them prisoner. The road lay for many days' journey through a haunted wilderness, but, mounted on his great horse Rakhsh, Rustam set out boldly.

On the first night, a lion came out of the desert, thinking to kill the horse and then devour the hero as he lay sleeping. But Rakhsh was on guard, and after a desperate battle killed the lion. When Rustam woke and saw the body, he thanked Rakhsh for his good service but blamed him for risking a single combat instead of calling on his master for help.

On the next day the sun beat fiercely, the desert was waterless, and horse and rider were fainting with thirst. But in answer to Rustam's prayer a ram appeared, which led them to a spring of water and mysteriously vanished. Rustam gave thanks, watered Rakhsh and washed him, quenched his own thirst and lay down to sleep after warning Rakhsh to wake him if any creature, whether friend or foe, appeared.

Little did he know that the spring belonged to a dragon, which crept upon the hero as soon as he was safely snoring with his head pillowed on his saddle. Again Rakhsh was on guard, and, faithful to his master's orders, woke him by stirring him with his hoof. Rustam sprang up and snatched his sword, but the cunning dragon, seeing that it had been foiled, slipped back into hiding. Rustam saw nothing, and after grumbling at Rakhsh for disturbing him, lay down again to sleep.

Again the dragon saw its opportunity and crept out; again Rakhsh faithfully woke his master; and again the dragon slipped back into hiding. This time Rustam was really angry; after searching for an enemy and finding none he thought that Rakhsh was playing a game with him, and threatened to cut his head off if he did not leave his master to sleep after his hard day's journey.

So when the dragon appeared a third time Rakhsh did not know what to do. Only when the monster was almost on his master did his loyalty overcome his fear, and once more he stirred Rustam with his hoof. Rustam sprang up in a fury, but this time the dragon was too close to escape. Sword in hand the hero attacked and made short work of his enemy.

Rustam finally reached the land of Mazanderan after many more adventures, rescued the king and his army, and killed the White Div, the chief of the demons.

RUSTAM & THE DRAGON, from a *Shah-nama*, 1576; London art market

Merlin and the Red Dragon and the White

Vortigern, who made himself High King of Britain after the departure of the Romans, did many foolish things and some wicked ones. For he brought in the savage Saxons from beyond the sea to defend his kingdom, and the Saxons turned against him and at last he was beset by enemies on every side. So he resolved to build a great and strong tower where he would be safe, and gathered all the masons of his realm for the work. But, however high they raised the walls in the day, every night they were cast down level with the ground.

At last the king's magicians told him that the tower would only stand firm if its foundations were set upon the body of a child who had no man for his father. Far and wide the king sought, and at last his men found the boy Merlin, whose mother was a noble and virtuous princess but whose father was a demon who had visited her in her dreams. So Merlin was brought to the tower, and when he saw the stones lying, with not one left upon another, he laughed. "Little would you laugh," said Vortigern, "if you knew for what end I had brought you here." "I laugh," said Merlin, "at your magicians, O King, who think that the body of a child will make firm the foundations of a tower built on a lake. Know that beneath this tower, for all that the ground seems firm, lies a great pool of water, and at the bottom are two dragons, a red and a white. It is their struggles that bring down the walls as fast as they can be raised. Dig beneath the tower and see."

The King thought it strange that Merlin should have known what fate had been plotted for him, so he told his men to dig as Merlin directed. At once, firm and dry though the ground had seemed, a great flood of water gushed out and spread until it became a huge pool. Then there was a hissing and a bubbling and the surface of the water was troubled, until all at once two huge fire-breathing dragons, a white and a red, broke the surface, locked in mortal combat. Finally the red dragon fled to the far end of the lake. "Alas for the red dragon," said Merlin. "Its destruction draws on apace. Its dens are occupied by the white dragon, which signifies the Saxons whom you have invited. The red dragon signifies the people of Britain, and shall be oppressed by the white."

(From Geoffrey of Monmouth, whose *History of the Britons*, written about eight hundred and fifty years ago, is the oldest source for many of the stories about King Arthur)

From Queen Mary's Psalter,
c. 1320; British Museum

Now all at once the waters of the lake vanished, and the king's masons raised his tower on the spot to which the red dragon had fled. But Vortigern was burned within his fortress by Ambrosius, who was afterwards remembered as the last of the Romans.

The brother of Ambrosius, Uther, was called Pendragon, or Dragon-head, because a fiery dragon appeared in the sky as sign that he should be king. He made two golden dragons, of which one was set in the chief church of his kingdom and one was carried with him into battle. His son, whom Merlin brought up until he came to the throne, was Arthur of the Round Table. Arthur's helmet is described by Edmund Spencer:

> For all the crest a Dragon did enfold
> With greedie paws, and over all did spred
> His golden wings: his dreadful hideous hed,
> Close couched on the bever, seem'd to throw
> From flaming mouth bright sparkles fierie red,
> That suddeine horror to faint harts did show;
> And scaly tayle was stretcht adown his back full low.

M for MERLIN from a manuscript from Canterbury, c. 1130; St. John's College MS. A, Cambridge; if you like illuminating letters with dragons, etc., you'll love Bellerophon's MEDIEVAL ALPHABET

Dragon Banners

From Trajan's Column, 113 A.D.

A Dragon Banner from the *Codex Aureus*, 9th century A.D.

KING HAROLD'S DRAGON STANDARD at
the Battle of Hastings, 1066; Bayeux Tapestry

Dragons were really used as battle-banners long before the days of King Uther Pendragon. The Romans, whose own standards were in the form of a golden eagle (there is one behind the Emperor Marcus Aurelius in the Bellerophon Book of Rome) fought against the northern peoples, who carried dragons, long serpents fashioned from brightly coloured cloth, which writhed and twisted in the wind as they were carried into battle. After the great emperor Trajan conquered Dacia, the country beyond the river Danube which has since been called Romania or "land of the Romans," he set up a column in Rome with the story of his victories carved in pictures round and round it. Here can be seen the Dacian dragons, with their heads fastened to poles and their long tails whipping in the wind behind, or dangling down despondently after the Romans have captured them and fastened them to their trophies. The column was set up in 113 A.D.

Two hundred and fifty years later, the strength of the legions was broken and the Roman army was filled with the horsemen of the north, who served for gold. The Emperor himself, as he rode among his officers, was recognized by the purple dragon that floated over his head. Uther's dragon-standard may have marked him as a Roman, as well as a British leader, and, on the other hand, the story of Sigurd Fafnirsbane may first have been told when the dragon-standards of the Empire were routed and its gold carried off by the northland kings.

The Saxons too thought of the dragon as a sign of war. Fiery dragons were seen in the sky above Winchilsea before the Vikings came, and no doubt the Saxon warriors thought that the dragon was just as real as the white horse which was shown on the king's standard. "Between the standard and the dragon" was the king's post on the battlefield, and here Harold Godwinsson, the last Saxon king, stood to meet the Normans at Hastings.

Perhaps many of the Norman knights as they rode up the hill on which the Saxon army was posted thought of their enemies' dragon-banner as a symbol of wickedness, and compared it with their own holy oriflamme, blessed by the Pope. For the minstrel Taillefer rode before them, tossing his sword into the air and catching it again and singing the song of Roland and Oliver, the paladins of Charlemagne, and their last battle against the infidel host with its dragon-banners—

> The Amir indeed was a man of might.
> He bade the Dragon be borne in his sight,
> And the banners of Termagant and Mahoun,
> And Apollyon also, the Evil One.
> Ahoy!

But even after the Conquest the dragon-banner was still carried before the Kings of England. The dragon of Richard the Lion Hearted terrified the Saracens, and late in 1306, when King Edward the Hammer of the Scots sent the Earl of Pembroke against Robert the Bruce, he ordered him

> "To burn and slay and raise dragon."

Finally in 1485, when the last Plantagenet lay dead on Bosworth Field, there came to the throne a king of Welsh blood who claimed descent from King Arthur. And now the two dragons were set as supporters on each side of the royal coat of arms.

Ardashir

This picture shows the dreadful fate of King Ardashir, who was attacked from behind by a dragon while he was riding in the mountains and gulped down before he had a chance to turn his horse. All the princes of the earth went into mourning for three months, so grieved were they that this noble monarch had perished so miserably.

SHAH ARDASHIR AND THE DRAGON, from the *Darabnama*, c. 1585; British Museum

Bahram

King Bahram Gur the great hunter spent the winter in feasting and song. But when spring filled the fields with tulips, he summoned a thousand Persian nobles to the chase. Two days they hunted the wild rams, the antelopes and the onagers, and when the light of the third dawn turned the mountains yellow and the meadows white there came against them a monstrous man-eating dragon. The fearless king first let fly his arrows and wounded the beast, then split open and slew it with a great blow of his sword. But he was himself blinded by the great flood of poison that poured out. Fortunately his horse carried him to an old peasant's hut. Nobody recognized him, but the old woman helped him wash off the poison.

BAHRAM GUR slaying the Dragon, from the *Shah-nama*, Shiraz, 1370; Sarayi Library, Istanbul

Sigurd and Fafnir

Fafnir the Dragon was the son of the giant Hreidmar. His brother Otter used to fish for salmon in a pool beside a waterfall, where he was killed by the god Loki. With his companions Odin and Hoenir, Loki came to Hreidmar's house, bringing Otter's skin. Hreidmar knew it as his son's, and demanded in payment enough gold to cover the skin so that not a hair of it could be seen. Now in the stream where Otter used to fish there lived a dwarf named Andvari, who had changed himself into a monstrous pike in order to guard a huge treasure of gold. Loki went to the stream and caught the pike in a net, and made him ransom himself with all his treasure except one gold ring. But when the gold was heaped on the skin, one hair from the tip of the tail still showed. So Loki went back to Andvari and took the last ring also.

This was a magic ring, which had the power to breed more gold, and Andvari, who had not minded the loss of the rest of the treasure so much, was filled with despair and bitterness and cursed the gold and whoever should possess it. Sure enough, for the sake of the treasure Hreidmar was slain by his own sons Fafnir and Regin, and Fafnir then seized all the gold for himself and carried it to a gloomy heath, where he guarded his hoard beneath his dragon-coils.

Regin was no warrior, but he was a skilled smith, and he was resolved to be revenged for his share of the treasure. So when the young hero Sigurd came to him, he promised to make him a sword with which he could slay the dragon. Sigurd might keep the gold: all Regin asked was his brother's heart to roast and eat.

The first sword that Regin forged shattered when Sigurd tried it on a lump of iron, and the second too. But his mother had kept the broken pieces of the magic sword Gram, the gift of Odin to Sigurd's father. From the pieces Regin fashioned a blade which split the lump of iron in two, and was so sharp that when Sigurd set it in a running stream it divided a lock of wool that floated down against it.

Though the sword was strong and sharp, the hero had still to come close enough to the dragon to deal him his death-blow, and that was no easy matter. Fafnir breathed out such fire and venom that no mortal man could stand before him. But, guided by Regin, Sigurd came to the heath where the dragon lay, and marked the track by which every day the monster crawled down to drink water. Here, right in the middle of the path, he dug a pit, in which he hid himself and waited. Presently he heard the dreadful noise of the dragon's coming: the earth shook and his fiery breath scorched the ground before him. But Sigurd lay safe in the pit until Fafnir was right over him: then he thrust the sword Gram through and through him and that was the end of the dragon.

As he had promised Sigurd put the dragon's heart on a spit and roasted it for Regin to eat. But it so chanced that when it was roasted he touched it with his finger, and, because it burned him, put his finger in his mouth. Hereupon he understood the speech of the birds, and learned from them that Regin was plotting to slay him by treachery. So at once he took off Regin's head.

SIGURD AND THE DRAGON from a carving from Hylestad Church, Norway

54

But the curse of Andvari followed him, and though he was a great hero and accomplished many adventures he came to sorrow and death in the end.

The picture was cut many hundreds of years ago into a great rock in Sweden. Sigurd, below, thrusts Gram through Fafnir. In the space surrounded by the dragon's coils Grani the hero's horse is tethered to the tree on which the birds sit. Sigurd, further to the left, has just tasted the dragon's heart and turns to hear what the birds are saying. Furthest left of all lies the headless corpse of Regin.

From the Ramsunberget rock, Sweden

Dietrich von Bern

The knight in this picture is said to be Dietrich of Bern, who comes in to the end of the story of Fafnir's treasure. In his youth he was a great hunter and slew dragons, elephants and other monsters. But I have not found a story that quite fits the top picture in any of the poems that I have read about him. The building on the right is perhaps a church. The runes under the lion who lies in front of it say "Here lies the mighty king whom the dragon killed." Perhaps the second lion is asking the knight to take vengeance on the dragon whom they are shown killing in the lower picture.

The poems tell how Dietrich became a great king and conquered Italy with the help of his friend Etzel. But in the end he was punished for his sins. As he was bathing one day in a stream, there appeared a wonderful stag, and at once he set his heart on hunting it. While he was wondering what to do, a horse trotted out of the forest, splendid to see and beautifully saddled and bridled, but as black as night from head to tail. Dietrich sprang onto its back, and at once it galloped off faster than the wind. Far and wide his men sought him, but Dietrich was never seen again, and at last it was agreed that the black horse was the Devil come to fetch him away. But some people said that the Devil had not carried Dietrich to his own place but into the wilderness, where he will fight against dragons until the Judgement Day.

(From *Thidrekssaga* and *Etzels Hofhaltung*: Dietrich and Etzel in these poems take their names from Theodoric King of the Ostrogoths and Attila the Hun, who were real people. But the stories that the poets tell were made up hundreds of years later: Theodoric was not even born when Attila died in 453 A.D.)

DIETRICH VON BERN from an Icelandic church door, c. 1230; *Thodminjasafn*, Reykjavik

The Red Cross Knight

Gloriana, the Fairy Queen, kept her annual feast twelve days, and on each of the twelve a different adventure was undertaken by one of her knights. The Red-cross Knight was a tall country boy who, after gaining from the Queen the promise of the first adventure, lay down on the floor because he was not worthy of a better place. Presently there came in a beautiful lady dressed all in mourning, followed by a dwarf who led a knight's war horse, on which was loaded a suit of armor. She begged the Queen to allow one of her knights to take the horse and weapons and go with her to rescue her father and mother, who were held prisoners by a cruel dragon in his castle of brass. The boy started up from the floor and claimed the adventure. The lady warned him that he must first prove himself able to bear her arms, but when he had put them on he seemed the best man in all the Queen's court. So the lady liked him well, and he was knighted and they set out together.

Here are some of the lines in which the poet Spenser describes the dragon, whom the Knight reached at last after defeating many other enemies on the way. They are written in the sort of English that was used four hundred years ago, and if you read them aloud and do not worry about the spelling I think you will understand them. "Pennes" in the fourth line means "feathers".

> His flaggy wings when forth he did display
> Were like two sayles, in which the hollow wynd
> Is gathered full, and worketh speedy way:
> And eke the pennes, that did his pinions bynd
> Were lyke mayne-yards, with flying canvas lynd.
>
> His huge long tayle wound up in hundred foldes
> Does overspread his long bras-scaly backe,
> Whose wreathed coils whenever he unfoldes
> And thicke entangled knots adown does slacke,
> Bespotted as with shields of red and blacke,
> It sweepeth all the land behind him farre,
> And of three furlongs does but little lacke;
> And at the point two stings infixed arre,
> Both deadly sharpe, that sharpest steele exceeden farre.
>
> And what more wondrous was, in either jaw
> Three rackes of yron teeth enraunged were......
>
> His blazing eyes, like two bright shining shields,
> Did burne with wrath, and sparkeld living fyre;
> As two broad Beacons, set in open fields,
> Send forth their flames farre off to every shyre...

This dreadful monster threw down the knight and his horse at their first meeting, and though they sprang up again, after a dreadful struggle at the end of the day hurled the knight into a well.

Gloriana

From an engraving by Thomas Cecill,
c. 1625-40. British Museum.

QUEEN ELIZABETH I, the descendant and lawful heir of UTHER PENDRAGON, tramples her enemies underfoot.

QUEEN ELIZABETH I tramples the Dragon, from the last medal of her reign

And clapt his yron wings, as victor he did dwell.

But the well was the Well of Life, which had power to heal all wounds and sickness, so next morning the Knight came out to battle fresh as before.

On the second day the Knight was again overthrown. But this time he fell into the precious balm that flowed from the Tree of Life. So again he was healed, and on the third day, when the dragon rushed on him to swallow him up, drove his sword through his open jaws and gave him a mortal wound.

So the Knight won the Lady Una.

Spenser tells us that the twelve Knights in his poem were each meant to stand for a special virtue. The Red-cross Knight was Holiness, who conquered sin. Gloriana stood for Glory in general, but also for "the most excellent and glorious person of our soveraine Queene"—that is, Queen Elizabeth I of England, and the knights and their foes were also Queen Elizabeth's knights and her enemies.

(From Edmund Spenser, *The Fairie Queene*)

THE REDCROSS KNIGHT from a woodcut for the first edition of *The Faerie Queene*

Saint Columba and the Loch Ness Monster

Once upon a time, when Saint Columba was staying for some days in the country of the Picts, he had to cross the River Ness. When he came to its bank, he saw some of the country people burying an unfortunate man who, so they said, a water-monster had seized as he was swimming, a short time before, and bitten with a most savage bite. Some of them had come to the rescue in a boat, and, though too late to save him, had pulled up his poor body with hooks. When the Saint heard this, he gave orders that one of his companions should swim over and bring to him the boat, which was on the opposite shore, so that he could cross. On hearing this command, Lugneus Mocumin without delay obediently took off his clothes, except his tunic, and plunged into the water. But the monster, so far from being satisfied, had been given an appetite for prey, and was lurking in the depths of the river. As the man swam, the monster felt the water disturbed above it, and suddenly coming to the surface with a great roar and jaws agape made for the swimmer as he was in mid-stream. All those who were present, not only the savages but the Brethren themselves, were overwhelmed with terror. But when the Saint beheld, he raised his holy hand and inscribed the Cross, the sign of salvation, in the empty air. Calling upon the name of God, he commanded the savage beast, saying: "Go no further! Do not touch the man! Go back at once!" Then the monster, hearing the words of the Saint, fled backwards in terror, faster than it had come, as though it were pulled by ropes. And it had come so close to Lugneus as he swam that between the man and the monster there was no more than a pole's length. Then the Brethren, seeing that the monster had retreated and that Lugneus their comrade had returned to them untouched and unharmed in the boat, marvelling greatly glorified God. And even the heathen savages who were present were overcome by the greatness of the miracle which they themselves had seen, and magnified the God of the Christians.

From Adamnan's *Life of Saint Columba*. This probably happened in about 565 A.D., soon after Columba began his mission to the Picts. Adamnan was born in 624 A.D., twenty-seven years after Columba's death, and may have talked with people who had known the Saint and his comrades. This

Sea Dragons and Monsters on a
Pictish stone from a little later than Saint Columba's time, from Murthly,
near the author's home in Scotland; now in the National Museum of Antiquities, Edinburgh

is the earliest mention of the Loch Ness Monster, which does not seem to harm people nowadays.

Lugneus Mocumin in his old age became Abbot of "the monastery on the Isle of Elena," though we do not know where that was.

Columba was a skilful writer of books, and people used to think that he wrote the "Book of Durrow," from which come the biting monsters in the picture below. But probably the "Columba" who wrote the book and prays that his name may be remembered lived about a hundred years after the Saint.

From the Book of Durrow, f 192 v, 7th century A.D. Trinity College, Dublin

Taniwhas

Taniwhas are monsters of deep waters and great rivers, about which the Maoris of New Zealand tell stories. They are said to resemble fishes, but to walk on four legs, and to be huge and terrible, so that they are clearly a sort of dragon. They may be good and friendly, but if they are injured in any way they take a dreadful revenge.

Tutaeporoporo, the Taniwha of the Whanganui River, had been cherished by the chief Tuariki. But his friend was killed by the Whanganui people, and he took up his abode in their river to punish them. Whole canoe loads of men and women were swallowed by him, and all the land was in terror.

At last there came to the Whanganui country a noble warrior of another tribe, named Aokehu. He loved a maiden of Whanganui, Hine-au-Moana, but when he spoke to her of his love she replied that she was betrothed already to a man of her own tribe; that if she were not her tribe would never consent to her marriage with a stranger; and finally that in any case she did not love Aokehu.

Soon after this Hine's people went to war, and the battle went against them and the man who was to marry Hine was killed. But in the nick of time Aokehu, who had followed the war-party, arrived on the battlefield and fought so valiantly that he turned defeat into victory.

Now he was honored by Hine's people, who were ready to give him whatever he asked for. But the girl said that there still remained the third obstacle to their marriage. She did not love him and never would unless he killed Tutaeporoporo the taniwha.

So Aokehu fashioned a great bowl of wood, and in this he floated down over the part of the river where the taniwha was usually to be found. All at once the monster rose from the depths, and with a single snap of its jaws bowl and man vanished. And now Hine, who was watching from the bank, found too late that she did indeed love him, and had sent him to his doom.

But suddenly the taniwha came to the surface again, struggling feebly, crawled ashore, and turned over to die. Out from its jaws stepped Aokehu, safe and sound. For when the monster swallowed him his bowl had protected him, and he had laid about him with his good knife until he dealt his enemy a mortal wound. So he saved Hine's people and won her love.

A carved Maori *taniwha* from Te Kuiti, New Zealand; 19th century

More Taniwhas

One day, about one hundred and fifty years ago, a ship came to New Zealand, and strange monsters were lowered from it into the sea, and swam ashore. The Maoris who saw ran for their lives, thinking that here indeed were mighty taniwhas. They shouted to warn the sailors who were rowing ashore in a small boat to get back to their ship before they were eaten.

But the sailors came stubbornly on and reached the shore safely. And now—horrors!—one of them actually slipped a rope over a taniwha's head and climbed on its back. At once the beast ran off into the woods. Obviously it was carrying the rash sailor away to its den to devour him. But no! back it came, and instead of eating the man it began to eat grass.

Now the sailors called the Maoris to come down, but they were all terrified and stayed shut in their fort except for one old man who said he was not afraid of any monster. The sailors set him on the taniwha, and again the beast set off and his friends sorrowed for the old man. But again the taniwha came quietly back and began eating grass.

Next the chief himself ventured a ride, and the upshot of it was that he bought two taniwhas from the sailors. Just in time too, for a stronger tribe in the neighborhood sent a war party over the hills. On they came, clashing their weapons and shouting insults, with their two champions out in front.

The defenders faced the enemy in silence, as though they were afraid. But when the other tribe drew close, suddenly the ranks opened and the two taniwhas came out with the defending champions on their backs. The attacking champions fell down flat on their faces, expecting to be eaten, and their friends never stopped running until they got home.

That is how the first horses came to New Zealand.

(From Sir Maui Pomare, *Legends of the Maori*)

The picture (turn the book sideways to look at it) shows how a New Zealand artist "saw" horses as taniwhas. This is part of a carving in the Otago Museum, Dunedin, showing the great New Zealand horse Phar Lap winning the Melbourne Cup. Phar Lap is the taniwha in front, and if you look carefully you will make out his jockey on his back. The beaten Australian horse comes behind.

Professor Anderson wrote the Bellerophon Book of HORSES & RIDING

Conclusion

"For the conclusion of the history of the dragon, we will take our farewell of him in the recitall of his medicinall vertues, which are briefly these that follow. First, the fatte of a Dragon dryed in the sunne, is good against creeping Ulcers: and the same mingled with Hony and Oyle, helpeth the dimnesse of the eyes at the beginning. The head of a dragon keepeth one from looking a squint: and if it be sette up at the gates and dores, it hath beene thought in auncient times to be very fortunate to the sincere worshippers of GOD. The eye beeing kept till they be stale, and afterwards beate into an Oyle with Hony and made into an onytment, keepe any one that useth it from the terrour of night-visions and apparisions.

But of all other, there is no folly comparable to the composition which the Magitians draw out of a dragon to make one invincible, and that is this. They take the head and tayle of a dragon, with the hayres out of the forehead of a Lyon, and the marrow of a Lyon, the spume or white mouth of a conquering horse, bound uppe in a Harts-skinne, together with a clawe of a dogge, and fastned with the crosse nerves or sinew of a Hart, or of a Roe; they say that this hath as much power to make one invincible, as hath anie medicine or remedy whatsoever.

The fatte of dragons is of such vertue that it driveth away venomous beastes. It is also reported, that by the tongue or gall of a dragon sodde in wine, men are delivered from the spirits of the night, called *Incubi* and *Succubi*, or else Nightmares. But above all other parts, the use of theyr blood is accounted most notable. But whether the *Cynnabaris* be the same which is made of the blood of the dragons and Elephants, collected from the earth when the dragon and the Elephant fell downe dead together, according as *Pliny* delivereth, I will not heere dispute, seeing it is already done in the story of the Elephant. And to conclude, *Andreas Balvacensis* writeth, that the Blood-stone, called the *Haematite*, is made of the dragons blood: and thus I will conclude the history of the dragon, with this storie following out of *Porphyrius*, concerning the good successe which hath beene signified unto men and women, eyther by the dreames or sight of dragons.

Mammea the Mother of *Alexander Severus* the Emperour, the night before his birth, dreamed that she brought forth a little dragon, so also did *Olympia* the Mother of *Alexander* the Great, and *Pomponya*, the Mother of *Scipio Affricanus*. The like prodigie gave Augustus hope that he should be Emperor. For when his mother *Aetia* came in the night time unto the Temple of *Apollo*, and had sette downe her bedde or couch in the Temple among other Matrons, suddainely shee fell asleepe, and in her sleepe, shee dreamed that a dragon came to her, and clasped about her bodie, and so departed without dooing her any harme. Afterwards the print of a dragon remained perpetually uppon her belly, so as she never durst more be seene in any bath.

The Emperour *Tyberius Caesar*, had a dragon which hee daily fedde with his owne handes, and nourished like good fortune, at the last it happened that this dragon was defaced with the byting of Emmets, and the former beautie of his body much obscured: Wherefore the Emperour grewe greatly amazed thereat, & demaunding a reason thereof of the Wisemen, hee was by them admonished to beware the insurrection of the common people. And thus with these stories, representing good and evil by the dragon, I will take my leave of this good and evil Serpent." *Topsell*